Using stories
to teach
Science

Ages 6–7

'CH

A division of MA Education Ltd

Steve Way visits schools presenting his science stories, maths stories and creative writing ideas. He gained a degree in Biological Sciences at Lancaster University before studying for his P.G.C.E.

Simon Hickton is Headteacher of Carcroft Primary School near Doncaster. He gained a degree in Biochemistry from York University before studying for his P.G.C.E..

Published by Hopscotch
A division of MA Education Ltd
St Jude's Church, Dulwich Road
Herne Hill, London SE24 0PB
Tel: 020 7738 5454

© 2008 Hopscotch Educational Publishing

Written by Steve Way and Simon Hickton
Series design by Blade Communications
Cover illustration by Debbie Clark
Illustrated by John Welding
Printed in the UK by CLE

ISBN 978-1-90539-025-0

Steve Way and Simon Hickton hereby assert their moral right to be identified as the authors of this work in accordance with the Copyright, Designs and Patents Act, 1988.

Contents

Introduction

About the series

The two books in the Key Stage 1 series *Using stories to teach science* use stories as a different but fun way of initiating a science lesson. The aim is for a science concept to be presented in a format that shows how science can relate to normal (or imagined!) life. The more ways, especially fun ways, we look at a subject we are learning, the more likely we are to come to understand it and to remember it!

Each book includes one story for each of the six main units of study in the DfEE/QCA *Scheme of Work for Science* that the children have to cover in science in that year, along with a suggested lesson plan and photocopiable resource sheets. These sheets are sometimes activity sheets or in other cases recording sheets. In each case, the story and its associated lesson could be used to introduce each unit or could be incorporated into the series of lessons you are planning for that unit of study. The suggested lesson plans are only a guide and so you can pick and choose the suggestions and ideas that will work best in your school or with your class.

Reading the story

When you read the story to the children, we recommend that you read it twice; the first time as a story in its truest sense – one they can listen to and enjoy as a piece of narrative, without it being broken up and dissected as it's told. Hopefully, the enjoyment they get from the story will enhance their enjoyment of the science they will be learning. However, on the first reading of the story, they may have been so involved in the plot and characters that they miss some of the science ideas that are used. So on the second reading you can get the children to focus on the science ideas that are woven into the story, by stopping at the points where a new science concept enters into the narrative and discussing its role in the story. If at all possible, enlarge a copy of the story and display it on an overhead projector as you are reading it. The children will then have the benefit of seeing the illustrations as you read and some may even be able to follow the text with you.

One extra story

'Holiday resort competition', on page 47, is an additional story on the theme of melting and freezing. It has been provided for you to use as an additional lesson on this theme (see the notes on page 51).

Using the lesson plans

Each lesson plan contains:
- ❑ The learning objectives, with the National Curriculum and Scheme of Work references;
- ❑ A list of the resources required;
- ❑ Whole class starter activities;
- ❑ Suggestions for individual, paired or group work;
- ❑ A plenary session;
- ❑ Further suggestions.

There are also three characters, known as WALT, WILF and TIB, who provide information.

 WALT stands for 'We Are Learning Today'.

 WILF stands for 'What I'm Looking For'.

 TIB stands for 'This Is Because'.

These or similar systems are often used to ensure lessons are focused, objective led and in context for the learner. They help summarise the purpose of the lesson, what is required of the children in order for them to successfully learn that lesson and why what they are learning is important.

The resource sheets have been designed to support the learning the children are making in science. Completing them will often require literacy skills, which in some cases the children will not have acquired as yet. In order that the work remains focused on science, we suggest that you, or your classroom assistants, scribe for such children so that their capability in science is not held back by specific difficulties with literacy. The investigative lessons support assessment for learning by enabling time for teachers and/or classroom assistants to record comments made by the children as they plan experiments, discuss predictions and so on.

We hope you enjoy using this book and that the ideas in it help add to your toolbox of resources for teaching science.

Science Scheme of Work objectives

Unit 2A: Health and growth

Section 2: Eating different types of food

Section 3: Planning a meal

NC: Sc2 2b, 2c

To understand that humans and other animals need food and water to stay alive. To understand that taking exercise and eating the right types and amounts of food help humans to keep healthy.

Background

This unit helps the children to find out and think about which foods contribute towards a healthy diet. It also helps them think about what quantity of each food type is healthy to eat and which foods should ideally only be eaten in small amounts, such as chocolate. (Unfortunately!)

This unit links with Unit 1A: Ourselves because a healthy diet is essential in promoting healthy growth and maintenance of all the body parts including the sense organs. Lack of Vitamin A in the diet causes an unbelievably distressing number of children to become blind.

Both a lack of or an excess of food are forms of malnutrition, cases of which are seen in almost all schools at some time, so clearly educating children about a proper diet is highly important. There are schools where all the children are obviously far smaller on average than the national norm and also where there are very young children who are quite outstandingly obese for purely dietary reasons. So in some cases the children's parents may need educating too. You could consider inviting them in to see the work the children have done, such as the class display that could result from this chapter. You could have information on hand from the local health authority/centre.

Resources

• Photocopiable activity sheets 1–3 (pages 10–12)

What to do

We are learning about a balanced diet.

❑ Tell the children that the story they are going to hear is a funny way of thinking about the different foods we eat and how good they are for us. Ask them to concentrate on the story as much as they can because you want them to remember which foods are mentioned in the story. Tell them that when you have read them the story you are going to make a class list of the foods mentioned in the story and put them into groups depending on which type of food they are.

❑ Read the story (pages 7–9).

❑ Make a table on the board using the following food categories:

A. bread, cereals, pasta, rice

B. fruit, vegetables

C. meat, fish, beans

D. dairy products *

E. fatty/sugary foods

*Even though it's a little different from butter we suggest you include margarine in this category for simplicity. As a source of fat it's generally better but it contains virtually no calcium.

❑ Ask the children which foods they can remember from the story and then ask them if they know which category on the table they go in. When you've agreed each one, add them to the list. Ask them if they can think of other types of food similar to the ones mentioned in the story and add them to the list.

❑ Ask the children if they know how these different types of food help us. Categorise them like this:

• Healthy energy foods (such as potatoes, rice, bread, pasta and cereals)
  For energy!

• Fruit and vegetables
  For good health

• Meat, fish and beans
  To help us grow

• Dairy products
  For bones and teeth

• Fatty/sugary foods
  By 'fatty foods' we mean foods that provide virtually no nutritional benefit other than an

excessive amount of calories, such as ice cream, cheesecake, crisps, burgers and mayonnaise. Some fat can be useful in the diet to provide energy for long-term activities (provided they are being done!) and insulation – as the cheese argues in the story. However, the children will get more than sufficient fat from eating some dairy products, margarine, meat and fish. There are only two essential fatty acids and these are only needed in tiny amounts (found in fish oil and some vegetables).

❑ Also, you could bring in various foods or pictures of various foods and ask the children to separate them into the different groups.

❑ Ask the children if they know how many normal servings of each type of food it is best to eat each day. It should be around:

A. Healthy energy foods: 2–3 servings

B. Fruit and vegetables: 5 servings (ask the children to watch out for the foods that are displaying the 'five a day' symbol)

C. Meat, fish and beans: 2 servings

D. Dairy products/margarine: 2–3 servings

E. Fatty/sugary foods: a small amount! 1 serving at the most!

Individual, paired or group work

❑ Write the above information on the board and then tell the children that you are going to give them recording sheets to complete to display this information. For example, they have to choose two or three carbohydrates from the list they have made and then draw or list them on the table on the worksheet.

I'm looking for you to be able to say what a balanced diet is made up of.

This is because a balanced diet keeps us healthy.

❑ Record sheet 1, for lower achievers, asks the children to complete the chart by drawing the appropriate number of particular types of food to make a healthy diet.

❑ Record sheet 2, for average achievers, asks the children to just write the names of an appropriate number of particular types of food to make a healthy diet.

❑ Record sheet 3, for higher achievers, requires the children to first write the names of the different types of food on the base of the table then complete the chart to show a healthy diet.

Plenary

❑ Review the work the children have done. Ask them if they can remember the names of the different types of food. Ask them if they can think of other measures we need to take to help us remain healthy, particularly drinking enough water and having enough exercise. As it is also a part of this unit you could discuss how it is important to use properly the medicines we are given by medical practitioners if we become ill.

Extension activities

❑ Provide the children with an A5 sheet of paper and ask them to draw foods from one of the food groups for a class diagram/display.

❑ The class could also produce a 'food pyramid'. One example can be found at www.caloriecounter.co.uk/diet_nutrition.

❑ For homework you could ask the children to prepare a menu for a healthy meal/a day's meals.

The foods in the Frier family's fridge were having a debate about which of them were best at keeping the Friers healthy.

'Well...' began one of the grapes.

'I must be one of the most important foods,' began the pasta, interrupting, 'because I give people lots of energy to do things, like the potatoes in the salad and the bread and rice in the cupboard. If people didn't get energy from food like me, they wouldn't be able to do anything!'

'Actually...' began another of the grapes.

'No, no, no!' interrupted the pork chops. 'We and the chicken legs must be the best foods because we help people grow and stay healthy.'

'Excuse me...' began another grape.

'Hey! Hang on a minute!' interrupted the red kidney beans in the vegetarian chilli. Our friends the chickpeas in the hummus and the baked beans in the cupboard help people grow and stay healthy too!'

'YEAH!' agreed the chickpeas in the hummus. 'And as David and Mary are vegetarian, you pork chops and chicken legs are only good for Paula and Ashley.'

'As it happens...' began yet another grape.

Fridge fight

'I... I think I'm quite important to the Friers' diet,' interrupted the cheese, slightly nervously.

'You? How can you be?' demanded the chicken legs, a little harshly. 'You're high in fat (unlike us, actually).'

'Well,' replied the cheese, a lot more confidently, 'everyone needs a little fat in their diet to store energy for activities like long walks or cycling. Also, I've got lots of something called calcium in me that helps build healthy bones and teeth. So as long as no one eats too much of me I'm very important!'

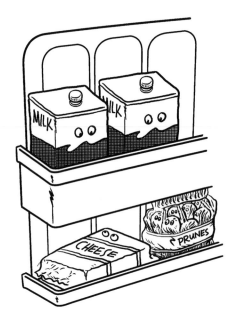

'Me too!' piped up the semi-skimmed milk. 'And I'm usually lower in fat than the cheese!'

'I think you'll find that we're quite important,' said the prunes, pompously. 'We're extremely important in helping move the food through someone's body from one end... to the other...'

'Could I just mention that...' began a fifth grape.

'Just a minute,' said the spring water, interrupting yet another poor grape. 'I'll have you know that people are mostly made up of water and if they don't drink enough of me they can become dehydrated. That means they haven't got enough water inside them. If they get dehydrated they can't think or play as well as normal. That's why children have water bottles with them in schools these days. So I think I'm the most important.'

'WILL YOU LOT SHUT UP!!!' shouted all the grapes in the bunch at once. 'We and the vegetables are important for keeping people healthy and they should eat five portions of us a day. We happen to know that what's most important is a balanced diet, where people eat a sensible mix of most foods.'

'Yeah!' agreed a carrot. 'As long as they don't eat too much salt, sugar or fat and have a balanced diet, that'll help most people stay healthy.'

'That's right!' piped up the sprouts. 'And as well as a healthy diet, people need regular exercise and time to rest.'

'But people can have some of me... every now and then... as a treat,' added the chocolate, who had been keeping quiet during this debate.

'Oh yes...' everyone agreed, encouragingly.

Suddenly, all the foods stopped speaking.

The fridge door opened and Ashley looked in.

'That's funny. I thought I heard a noise in here,' he said to his mum.

'Oh Ashley, you're always imagining such crazy things...' replied Paula as Ashley got some grapes out of the fridge. He didn't notice the pork chops wink at the pasta as he closed the door.

Name _____

A healthy diet

Complete the chart by drawing pictures of different foods to make a healthy diet.

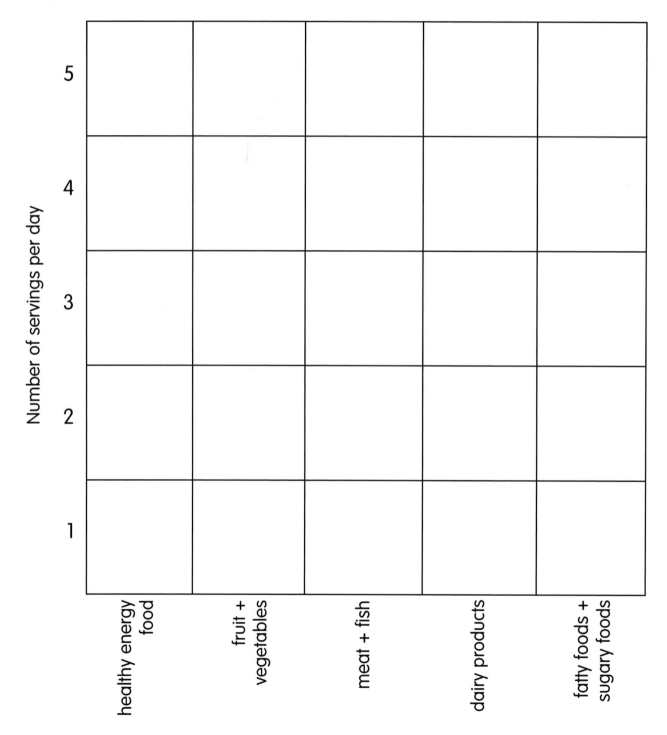

Number of servings per day

5

4

3

2

1

healthy energy food

fruit + vegetables

meat + fish

dairy products

fatty foods + sugary foods

Different groups of food

Name _____

A healthy diet

Complete the chart by writing the names of different foods to make a healthy diet.

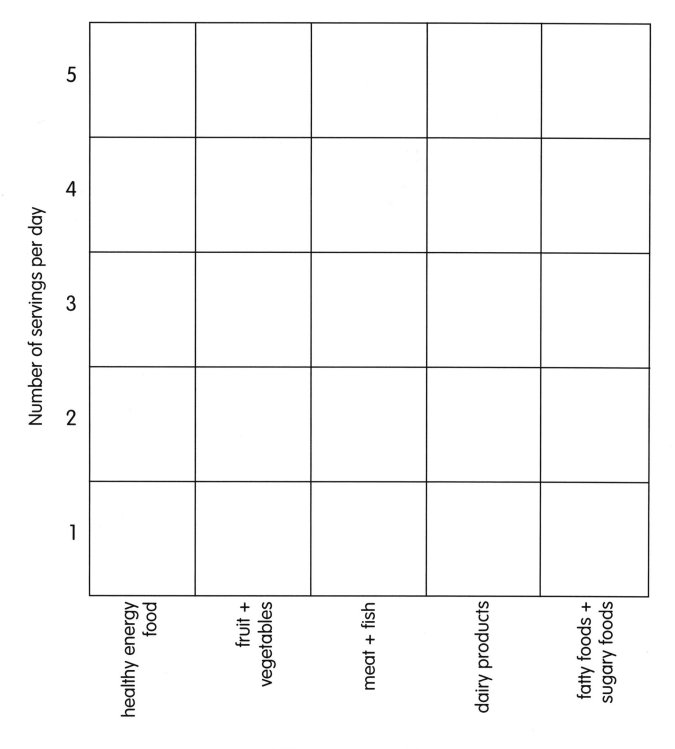

Name _____

A healthy diet

Write the names of the different food groups at the bottom of the table. When you've done this then fill in the correct number of blocks in the table by writing the names of the different foods that make a healthy diet.

5					
4					
3					
2					
1					

Number of servings per day

Different groups of food

Science Scheme of Work objective

Unit 2B: Plants and animals in the local environment

Section 2: Looking for plants and animals

NC Sc2 5a

To find out about the different kinds of plants and animals in the local environment.

This lesson asks the children to think about something that they don't often realise, particularly in urban schools; that it is very likely that quite a large number of plants and animals could be living all around them in their local environment.

The story is intended to be a kind of leg-pulling idea. The television presenter in the story, Simple Simon, quite obviously passes lots of plants and animals without registering that that's what they are. Perhaps the children are doing the same thing too!

Although it's hugely important to preserve the world's precious and unique ecologies, like charity it often begins best at home. By the children being more aware of the living organisms around them they may learn to appreciate their environment more and care for it more thoughtfully.

Resources

• Photocopiable activity sheets 1–3 (pages 17–19)

• Red and green pens/pencils

What to do

We are learning that there are a lot of different plants and animals all around us.

❑ Explain to the children that the purpose of today's lesson is to think about the plants and animals that might be found all around them. Tell them that we can often forget how many plants and animals may be living all around us, even if we live in a fairly built-up area and not in the countryside, where we might normally expect to find quite a lot of wildlife.

❑ Tell the children that in the story you are about to read them, the main character, a television presenter called Simple Simon, comes across lots of plants and animals without properly noticing them. Say that after you have read the story you are going to ask them to help you list all the plants and animals that Simple Simon comes across, so they need to listen carefully.

❑ Read the story (pages 15–16).

❑ List all the animals and plants that Simple Simon fails to spot.

❑ Ask the children if they think they've ever walked around their local environment and managed to not realise how many plants and animals there are around them just like Simple Simon did.

Individual or paired work

❑ When you have completed the list, tell the children that you are going to give them an activity sheet on which they have to either complete or make up stories that could be set in their local environment. When they write the name of a plant they have to use the green pen/pencil you are going to give them. When they write the name of an animal they have to write it in red. Read through the sheets with the children before they start work on them. As the sheets contain a lot of text, or require the children to write a lot of text, it would be advisable to have an assistant working with them.

I'm looking for you to be able to tell the difference between plants and animals.

This is because we need to understand the world around us.

The local environment

- Activity sheet 1, for lower achievers, uses cloze procedure, requiring the children to fill in the gaps in a simple story similar to the one they have heard. The missing words are the names of either plants or animals. As completing this sheet requires a fair amount of literacy skills, it would be best if you or a classroom assistant could help the children to do it.

- Activity sheet 2, for average achievers, requires the children to write their own story along the lines of the one they have just heard, using the names of animals and plants mentioned in the story if they wish.

- The higher attainers' worksheet also requires the children to write their own story but in this case they are asked to use plants and animals that didn't feature in the story.

Plenary

- Ask the children if the work has made them more aware of the plants and animals that may be living all around them. If (hopefully) they think this is so, ask them if they can think of ways that they could help look after their local environment and the plants and animals living in it. You could go on a walk around your local environment and make a list of all the plants and animals living in the environment around the school.

Extension activities

- A fun way of emphasising what the children have learned is to ask them to do Activity sheet 1 again but this time deliberately putting the wrong names in the spaces. They will need to know the properties of the plants or animals to know how to make the story nonsense.

- You could play 'animal snake' or 'plant snake'. One of the children has to write the name of an animal or a plant. The next person has to use the last letter of that word to write the name of another animal or plant. For example:

```
L I O N
      E
      W
      T O R T O I S E
                    L
                    E
                    P
                    H
                    A
                    N
                    T
```

- Discussing the names of the children's choice of animals and plants could help to develop the whole class's knowledge of different plants and animals. Make sure that the children know some facts about the different plants and animals used.

Good morning. Welcome to 'Simple Simon Investigates'.

Today I'll be asking the question, 'Animals and plants – where are they?' Many people think that to find animals and plants you have got to travel many miles into the heart of the countryside but I'm going to see if I can find any wildlife along this footpath on the edge of town.

BUMP!

OW!

Honestly! Who put that tree there? That hurt! I was so busy looking into the camera that I didn't notice it. Anyway… now I've walked past this oak tree, I'll continue my search for animals and plants. Hang on, there are loads of ants underfoot, all helping each other carry a leaf. They're probably taking it back to their nest, I expect. I'd better step over them carefully before I continue my search.

Good grief! This footpath is really overgrown with grass, brambles, wild flowers and nettles… I must say they're really slowing down my hunt for wildlife.

Whoa! That was a bit of a shock! Two rabbits just shot across the path in front of me! I must have disturbed them in my hunt for wildlife. I wish I could find some… still, at least all that

Where's the wildlife?

lovely birdsong makes a pleasant background sound to my search.

Ow! Hey, can you believe it! An acorn just fell on my head! I think it was dropped by that squirrel that's jumping through the branches up there.

Whoa! Excuse me! I had to duck down there as a swallow swooped down right above me! Gosh, that was quite an exciting part of my hunt for wildlife… I just wish I could find some soon.

Well, I've come to the end of the footpath, without seeing any wildlife as far as I know, and now I've come to some fields. No wildlife here, I'm afraid. The field I'm in is full of barley… and in the field over there, on the other side of that hedgerow with berries in it, is corn… and all I can see in the next few fields are ordinary cows, sheep, horses and chickens.

So, sorry folks, it does seem that wildlife is very difficult to find. I think I need a sit down after all that searching. I know – the park's just over there. I'll go and sit down on that bench by the lovely rose bush and watch people going by walking their dogs or looking at the goldfish in the pond.

Bye bye.

Name _____

Plants and animals around us

Complete the story by writing the missing words. Use the words in the box below to help you. Write the names of plants in green and the names of animals in red.

As John was running in the park he bumped into a _____.

'I won't do that again,' he thought as he watched a _____ with a big fluffy tail running through its branches.

He walked past a woman walking her _____.

As there were lots of them, he picked his mum some _____ that were growing in the _____.

'Mustn't pick them unless there are lots,' he thought, as he watched an army of _____ running about on the ground.

Then John walked home. All the way home he watched the _____ swooping through the sky.

When he got home he saw that his mum was pruning the _____.

Just before he went to bed he remembered to feed the _____ in the bowl.

goldfish	ants	dog	daisies	tree
grass	squirrel	swallows	rose bush	

Name _____

Plants and animals around us

Write a story like the one you've just heard. You could use the plants and animals in the box below or you could use your own.

Write the names of plants in green and the names of animals in red.

Try to have as many animals and plants as possible in your story.

Write a title for your story.

_____

_____

_____

_____

_____

_____

_____

_____

_____

_____

_____

_____

oak tree	wild flowers	squirrels	corn	chickens
ants	nettles	swallows	cows	rose bushes
grass	rabbits	barley	sheep	dogs
brambles	birds	berries	horses	goldfish

Activity sheet 2

Name _____

Plants and animals around us

Write a story like the one you've just heard. Use different plants and animals from the ones in that story.

Write the names of plants in green and the names of animals in red.

Try to have at least five animals and five plants in your story.

Write a title for your story.

_____

_____

_____

_____

_____

_____

_____

_____

_____

_____

_____

_____

_____

_____

_____

_____

_____

Activity sheet 3

Variation

Science Scheme of Work objectives

Unit 2C: Variation

Section 5: Measuring differences between children

NC Sc2 2a, 4a

To recognise similarities and differences between themselves and others and to treat others with sensitivity.

This unit gives the children the opportunity to explore some of the ways in which they vary from each other and to appreciate this variation. They then record some of the ways in which they vary from each other using a bar chart.

Variation of individuals is very important for the survival of a species. In the story, the characters from 'Same Planet' are essentially like clones. Relatively few species on Earth can clone themselves. Most species depend on having variety in form brought about by the mixing of genetic information during sexual reproduction. This variety of form means a greater chance of the species surviving if conditions become harsh, as some of the individuals may be able to cope with the tough conditions and parent the next generation. Even species that can clone themselves, such as greenfly or strawberry runners, only do so when conditions are favourable and the population can benefit from being able to capitalise on these conditions until they change. Carefully noticing and cataloguing the variation between individuals contributed to Darwin developing his momentous theory of evolution.

Of course, variation between people is also something to enjoy beyond the biological benefit it gives to our survivability. Appreciating variation between themselves and others in a positive way helps children to avoid developing the prejudices that indicate unwillingness to appreciate the differences of others – in other words, all forms of prejudice.

Resources

- Photocopiable activity sheets 1–3 (pages 25–27)
- Metre rules/wall measures for measuring height of children
- Class list for each group
- ICT graphics package (optional)

What to do

We are learning about the differences between ourselves and others.

What I'm looking for is for you to compare and record some of the differences between people in our class.

This is because we need to appreciate ourselves and each other and the differences between us.

❏ Explain to the children that this lesson will involve them thinking about how wonderful it is that we're all different from each other and then measuring and recording some of the ways in which we are.

❏ Tell them that the story is written in the form of a letter, from a child about their age called Sally Same, who lives on a planet where everybody and everything are all the same. Ask the children to listen out for what Sally thinks about living on Same Planet and also what she thinks it must be like living on Planet Earth. Tell them that after you have read the story you are going to ask them where they would rather live – on Planet Earth or Same Planet – and why.

- Explain the meaning of the word 'clone' (all the offspring are exactly like their adults, except younger). Obviously there are no human examples (yet!) but you could talk about how some gardeners cut a few leaves off a plant and then grow exact copies of the original plant.
- Read the story (pages 22–24).
- Ask the children which planet they'd prefer to live on! If some of them are daft enough to suggest 'Same Planet' get them to think about what it would be like if they lived there all the time. Ask the children to think about why we should be glad that we're all different from each other.

Group work

- Tell the children that you're going to divide them into groups (of different abilities) and that each group is going to collect information about the differences between various aspects of their bodies and then record that information on a bar chart. One group will be recording the number of people with particular eye colours, another the range of hair colours and the third the children's heights. Ask the children what problems there might be when they begin recording hair colours (and possibly eye colours) – i.e. the fact that each person's hair is a different colour. Explain to them that they need to agree on a range of colours to group people in, such as 'brown', but to remember that the results they produce will only give part of the picture that explains how hair colour varies in the class. Explain that scientists sometimes have to make difficult decisions like this about how to collect information and this means that there may be more than one way of looking at the information they discover. (Scientists aren't demigods whose pronouncements should be taken as gospel!)
- Ask the children why each group needs to have a list of everyone in the class. (So that everyone is observed/measured and isn't observed twice by the same group.)

We are learning how to record experimental results in a table.

We are going to make careful observations or take measurements and record them in a table so other scientists can read our results.

- Activity sheet 1, for lower achievers, asks the children to make a tally of the different eye colours in the class so they can then complete a block graph. Space is given to add any eye colours agreed by the group.
- Activity sheet 2, for average achievers, requires the children to make a tally of the different hair colours. Before beginning their tally they have to decide on the names of colours they will use to describe their hair. When they've collected their information they need to record it on a block graph.
- Activity sheet 3, for higher achievers, requires the children to measure the heights of children in the class, group each of these within a range of heights and record this information on a block graph.

Plenary

- Ask the different groups to show the class the block graphs they produced and explain what they discovered/what the graph shows about how these features vary within the class. Ask them to think of other things they could have measured (hand span, weight). Ask them if they now appreciate how fantastic it is that we're all different and that we don't live on Same Planet!

Extension activity

- The children could write a reply to Sally Same, explaining more about the differences between people, plants and animals on Planet Earth.

Same Planet

41 Same Villas,
Sametown,
Same County,
Same Land,
Same Planet,
SA ME

4th Samember 6413b

Dear Human Race,

I am writing to you after visiting your wonderful planet where your animals and plants, even those of the same kind, are all so excitingly different from each other. Also, most incredible of all – you humans are so fantastically different from each other that we on Same Planet can't believe it!

You see, here on Same Planet we're all nearly exactly the same as each other. The only difference is that some of us are older or younger than the other Samans (as we call ourselves). So I look exactly like my older samer (we don't have brothers or sisters like you do – that must be such fun), a lot like my parent and quite a lot like my grandparent. In fact I look a lot like everyone else on the planet!

We are all the same height and weight when we're born and we never get any bigger or smaller. I believe you do something called 'growing' that sounds very strange. Do you wake up in the morning and hit your head on the ceiling if you've done lots of growing overnight? We all have the same little tuft of purple hair growing out of the top of our head and eyes that are yellow with green spots.

Now maybe you might think it would be great to all be the same but I can tell you it isn't. I noticed that on Earth you often have phases called 'fashions' where you all try and look the same as each other. How silly that seems to us. You should all be delighted to be different from everyone else.

You see, because we're all the same, if one of us gets a cold… soon every single one of us has got it. No one wins or loses any games because we're all as good as each other, so playing team games isn't very exciting because almost all the games end in a draw. Also, none of us ever comes up with any original ideas that the rest of us can enjoy or benefit from because we all think in the same way.

As well as that, each of the animals, vegetables and trees that we have on our planet is the same, which is very boring and which often causes us several problems. Can you imagine how all our woods seem very uninspiring after a while because they're all exactly the same, with just the same tree growing in them wherever you go? It's almost pointless going anywhere on holiday because everywhere looks the same as everywhere else!

Same Planet

The animal we keep for food (called a swig – it's similar to your pig) has the same problems as us if it gets ill. If just one swig gets ill, within days all the other swigs are ill too. We also have frequent problems because we all eat the same vegetables – called samatoes – and if there's a bad crop one year because the conditions haven't been right for them (and guess what, they all have to have the same conditions) then we all go hungry.

So if you ever think people, animals or plants on your planet should all be the same, you come and visit us on Same Planet. You'll soon realise how wonderful it is that all the living things on your planet are different from each other. We're only two galaxies away (turn left at Pluto).

Yours,

Sally Same

Sally Same

Name _____

We are all different

Make a tally below of the number of people with different eye colours in your class. If your group agrees on more colours than the ones that are listed, add those colours to the list. Then complete the bar chart below.

Colour	Tally
Blue	
Grey	
Green	
Brown	

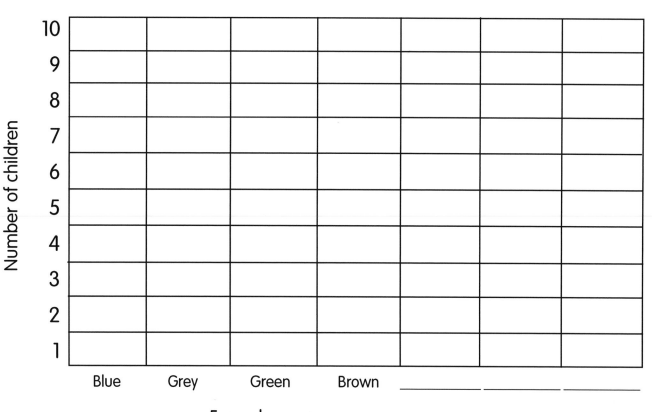

Eye colour

Activity sheet 1

Name _____

We are all different

Make a tally of the number of people with different hair colours in your class. Before you start you will have to decide the names of the colours you are going to record. Then use your tally to make a block graph.

Colour	Tally

Number of children

10
9
8
7
6
5
4
3
2
1

_____ _____ _____ _____ _____ _____

Hair colour

Name _____

We are all different

You are going to record the different heights in your class.
Make a tally of the number of people of different heights, within the ranges below.

Height range	Tally
50-60cm	
61-70cm	
71-80cm	
81-90cm	
91-100cm	
101cm or more	

Now use your tally to make a block graph.

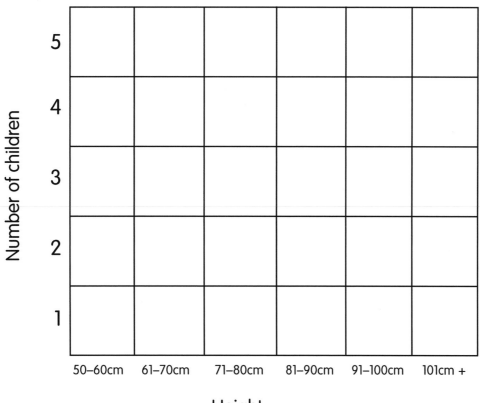

Height

Materials

Science Scheme of Work objectives

Unit 2D: Grouping and changing materials

Section 6: Melting ice

Section 7: Experimenting with melting ice

Section 8: Recording observations

NC: Sc3 2b

To explore melting ice using appropriate senses. To use results to draw a conclusion about which place is warmest.

This lesson involves looking at materials, in this case ice, making predictions about how quickly it will melt under certain conditions.

Making predictions and then testing them are key components of scientific enquiry. Basically, to be a good scientist you have to keep on wondering about things. 'I wonder if...?', 'I wonder what...?' and 'I wonder why...?' are the key questions that make the scientific world go round (provided you then go and see if you can find the answer to your questions!) Einstein said 'Imagination is everything,' which seems a fair comment from someone who could imagine what happens when you travel at light speed (such as time slowing down!)

It is important for children to understand that when we make predictions we don't have to be correct. Predictions just allow us to throw the stick forward and see what happens. A professional scientist should be just as excited when they find out their prediction is wrong as if they find out their prediction is correct. More so, even – they may have discovered that whatever it is they are studying is more interesting and complex than they thought. (Of course, it doesn't always work that way but the more we emphasise to the children that scientists should shout 'Hooray' whatever the results of their experiments, the less unnecessarily competitive/self-conscious they may be about making their predictions.)

The poem is about a girl called Loopy Leticia, who eats her ice lolly so slowly it melts all over her. To prevent it melting she goes to eat it in the fridge!

Resources

- Record sheet for making predictions and recording results (page 31)
- Equal sized ice cubes (or ice lollies)
- Different ice shapes
- Five equal sized dishes to put ice cubes in
- Clock timer

What to do

We are learning about the properties of materials.

Note: before the lesson you will need to make some ice cubes.

❑ Tell the children you are going to read them a silly poem about a girl who took so long to eat her lolly that it dripped everywhere.

❑ Read the poem (page 30).

❑ Discuss the different ideas Leticia had to stop the lolly from melting. What did she do in the end? What do the children think of her? **Make sure they understand that it was a funny thing for her to do in the poem but very dangerous to do in real life, including getting inside abandoned freezers because the can suffocate inside them.**

❑ Now tell the children that they are going to do an experiment to see how quickly ice cubes melt in different places. Explain that what you want them to do is predict which location will make the ice melt the quickest. Explain that making predictions is a key part of being a scientist and that, while we aim to make our predictions as accurate as possible, using the knowledge and experience that we have, it's all right if our predictions turn out not to be completely correct. Explain that this is because we have discovered – or are on the way to discovering – something new that we didn't know before. If we didn't make predictions and then test them, we would never know if we were correct or find out that there are more interesting things for us to discover and learn.

❑ Agree on five places to leave the dishes; for example, in the freezer if you have one, in the fridge/cool box, on a radiator, in the room away from the radiator, wrapped up in something 'warm'. (This last suggestion could be a way of introducing the idea that insulating materials can keep things cool as well as warm.)

❑ Ask the children why you are using equal sized containers to put the ice cubes in (to make the experiment a fair test). Ask them how else the experiment can be made fair (same sized ice cubes, equal number of ice cubes). Decide how often you are going to look at the ice cubes (about once every ten minutes seems sensible), agree what you mean by 'melted' (for example, no tiny fragments of ice remaining) and ask why you need to agree on these things before beginning the experiment.

What I'm looking for is for you to be able to predict and record the results of an experiment.

This is because scientists often make predictions and then test them as a way of finding things out.

Individual, group or paired work

❑ Hand out the recording sheet to the children in groups, pairs or as individuals. As a class, discuss and make a prediction about which will be the location that causes the ice to melt the fastest. Make sure the children write the name of that location as the first location on their list on the sheet.

❑ Then ask the children to work in pairs, predicting the order of the other locations, from the ones that cause the fastest melting to the ones that cause the slowest melting. This will mean that they will all have to think carefully about their predictions, rather than leaving the effort of predicting to the most outspoken members of the class.

❑ For the purpose of assessment and record keeping, you and your staff could record the comments the

children make to each other as they make their predictions.

❑ Choose children to take the dishes to each location. Set the timer going and after the agreed period of time send children to look at the ice cubes in the different locations and report back as to whether they have melted or not or what amount has melted. While you are waiting for the ice cubes to melt you could produce the ice shapes and ask the children to make predictions about how their shapes will change as they melt. You could have a shape for each table/group so they can draw it just as it starts melting and after it has been melting for a while.

❑ As the ice cubes melt, make a record on the board showing which cubes melted fastest and which slowest. Ask the children to record the results on their sheets, compare them with their predictions and reflect on the accuracy of their predictions.

❑ Discuss with the children the success or otherwise of their predictions. If the results were different from those they had predicted, ask them to consider why this might be.

❑ The sheet also asks the children to consider why they were correct or otherwise in their prediction of the outcome of the experiment. Their work will therefore be differentiated by outcome in terms of the quality of the answers given.

Plenary

❑ Read the poem again to the children.

❑ Ask them to see if they can think of any ways Leticia could prevent her lolly melting other than by eating it more quickly or sitting in the fridge!

❑ Ask the children what it means if the ice cubes melt very slowly or very quickly. Be sure that they understand that where they melt the most quickly must be the warmest place.

Extension activity

❑ Having seen the different ice shapes melting, the children could be asked to design shapes that might melt very quickly or very slowly. They could also make predictions about what would happen and, if possible, test these predictions.

❑ The additional story on pages 47–50 also looks at melting and freezing.

Loopy Leticia's Long-Lasting Lolly

Loopy Leticia liked lazily licking her lemonade lolly,
With languorous, loving, long luscious licks.
As the weather got warmer from the middle of May,
Loopy Leticia bought a lolly each day.
But poor little Leticia some sadness she felt,
For she took so long to lick it, it started to melt.

As the ice turned to water in her lemonade lolly,
It dripped everywhere, which wasn't too jolly.
So she ended up in a sticky wet mess,
As her lolly ended up all over her dress.
Somehow it oozed all over fingers and feet...
The worst thing though was, there was less lolly to eat!

'If only I could buy one when it's starting to snow,'
Whined the sticky young lady as she watched the sun glow.
'Or eat down in the cellar, where it's always quite cool.'
(Then she thought of the spiders, so she wasn't a fool.)
'Or, I wonder, would my family disapprove,
If to the freezing North Pole I suggested we move?'

Then our heroine had a different idea.
Another mad one, I rather do fear.
Later as her mum came through the kitchen door,
She noticed some odd things all over the floor.
The milk and yoghurt were stacked up looking neat,
And the salad and butter were right under her feet!

As she opened the fridge to peer inside,
The view that she saw made her go goggle-eyed!
Perched on a shelf with an icicle on her nose,
There was Leticia with blue hands and blue toes!
You might think her mother would have gone wild
But she controlled herself and said, 'Silly child!

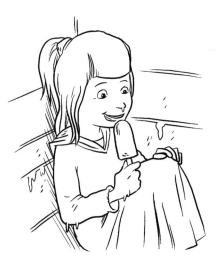

'If you want to have a lolly on such a hot day,
You'll have to stop it melting in some other way!
Maybe if you ate it faster than a snail,
Then you wouldn't leave behind you such a sugary trail.
Now go upstairs and put on a nice new clean dress...
Then come back downstairs AND TIDY UP THIS MESS!!!!!'

Name _____

Melting ice cubes

You are going to put some ice cubes in different places to see where they melt the fastest and the slowest.

Complete the list to show where you think the ice cubes will melt the fastest, through to where you think they will melt the slowest.

FASTEST   1. _____

              2. _____

              3. _____

              4. _____

SLOWEST   5. _____

~~~~~~

Complete the list to show which place caused the ice cubes to melt the fastest, through to the place where the ice cubes melted the slowest.

FASTEST   1. _____

              2. _____

              3. _____

              4. _____

SLOWEST   5. _____

Put a ✔ by your predictions that were right. Describe how accurate your predictions were. Were you surprised by any of the results?

_____

_____

_____

Record sheet

Forces and movement

• • • • • • • • • • • • • • • • • •

Science Scheme of Work objective

Unit 2E: Forces and movement.

Section 5: Experimenting with toy cars

Section 6: Presenting results

NC Sc4 2a

To find out about and describe the movement of familiar things; for example, cars going faster.

In this lesson the children are asked to think about how they can set up a fair test about toy cars rolling down a slope and then carry out the experiment, making recordings. The story acts as a stimulus for discussion because the children in the story carry out their experiments in a way that isn't sensible or fair.

One of the children cheats in the way that she carries out the experiment, which obviously confounds the results. Another child only records the results that suit his purposes and not the ones that don't and none of the children plans the sequence of slopes they test in an organised or logical way, further confounding the results. None of the children records the range of results that occur in the experiments (they only record the furthest distance travelled) so the variability of results also isn't acknowledged.

Sadly, some 'real' scientists have been guilty of all these sins before, so eliminating these and other bad habits from the children's scientific approach as early as possible is an important thing to do! Science as a discipline has much to offer but only if it's carried out in a rigorous manner. (Phew! Lecture over!)

One of the most important things to emphasise is the importance of keeping all the conditions the same in each series of experiments, except the thing we are changing (the 'dependent variable').

This experiment shows that, up to a certain height, the steeper the slope the further the car will travel or the faster the car will travel.

Resources

- Record sheet for each group (page 37)
- Equal length slopes to roll cars down (6)
- Plastic bricks or other regular shaped supports for slopes (21)
- Toy cars (6)
- Metre sticks (6)

What to do

We are learning how to carry out experiments taking measurements and recording them.

❑ Tell the children that the story they are going to hear is a funny story that looks at how some children did an experiment with lots of things wrong with it. Ask them to listen carefully so that they can tell you the different things that were wrong with the experiment. Show theM a toy car, similar to the one narrating the story.

❑ Read the story (pageS 34–36).

❑ Ask the children to help you list all the things the children did wrong in their experiment. This should include:

  – Claire gave the car a push even though the children had decided not to push it but just let go.

  – Ricky measured how far the car travelled down his slope even though it crashed and bounced most of the time.

  – The children only recorded the furthest distance the car travelled and didn't record the other distances.

  – The children only measured the distances travelled down three different slopes and the difference in the slopes didn't follow an ordered pattern (i.e. they used 2 bricks, 7 bricks and 4 bricks to support the slopes).

❑ As the children recognise each error, ask them to explain how the experiment should have been organised differently to make it a better experiment.

❑ Tell the children that you are going to ask them to conduct experiments testing the movement of toy cars down a slope. Ask them to think of other things to make the test fair. For example:

- Using the same car in each of their experiments;
- Using slopes of the same length;
- Using slopes propped up by the same kind of brick/support.

Extension activity

❑ The children could be asked to think of other experiments they could do using toy cars (for example, to compare how far different cars travel down the same slope) and explain how they would make their experiments fair.

What I'm looking for is for you to be able to set up a fair experiment.

This is because it's important for scientists to carry out fair experiments.

Group work

❑ Tell the children that you are going to divide them into six groups (of about five children). Each group will be responsible for setting up one of the slopes. For example, Group One will set up the slope propped up with one brick/support. They will then let their car roll down their slope three times, measure how far it travels from the end of the slope and record the results on the record sheet you will be giving them. Then each group will move from slope to slope in a carousel system, measuring and recording results for each slope. Finally, as a group they will be asked to consider the results of their experiment, using the questions on the record sheet as a stimulus.

Plenary

❑ Discuss the results of the experiments with the children. Ask them why they had to repeat the experiment twice for each slope. Ask them to explain why the experiment they carried out was so much better than the experiment carried out by the children in the story.

A toy car called Tommy

Phew! What a day! Hello children. My name's Tommy the Toy Car. Thank goodness it's half past three at the school I live in and the children have all gone home! You see, three of the children have been doing experiments using me all afternoon!

They wanted to know which would be the best slope to roll me down to make me move the fastest so I rolled the furthest along the floor at the bottom of the slope.

Well, Cautious Claire – she didn't think the slope would need to be very high but when she rolled me down the slope, which she'd raised off the floor by using only two bricks underneath the board, I hardly picked up any speed, so I hardly went any distance along the floor.

I think that Claire was disappointed because when her friends weren't looking she gave me a little push as she rolled me down the slope. I didn't think that was very fair – do you? The children had all agreed before they started doing their tests to just let go of me at the top of each slope because they thought it would be difficult to measure how hard they pushed me.

Of course, with a bit of a push to get me moving I did go further along the floor and Claire said, 'Told you so!' to her friends. She must have forgotten that when you do experiments it doesn't matter whose idea was right beforehand. It's much more interesting to know what really happens.

Then Reckless Ricky tried out his slope. He put seven bricks under one end of the slope and then rolled me down it. Well now, it was such a steep slope that when I zoomed down it I crashed at the bottom! That hurt, I can tell you – no wonder I'm tired! Sometimes I just ended up on my roof at the bottom of the slope but a few times I bounced as I hit the floor (OW!) and flew off in all sorts of directions.

Ricky insisted on measuring how far I'd gone away from the end of the slope even though I never carried straight on when I got to the bottom of it. Somehow I didn't think that was fair – what do you think?

Then Sensible Selina rolled me down the slope when she'd put four bricks underneath it. This time I picked up more speed than I did on Claire's slope but not so much that I crashed when I got to the bottom like on Ricky's slope. The only times I went further were when Claire was secretly pushing me and once when I crashed and then bounced after going down Ricky's slope.

A toy car called Tommy

At the end of the day though, none of the children could agree which was the best slope to use and I could hear them arguing about their experiments even after they had gone out of the school gates.

Well, I don't know about you but I think I know which was the best slope to use. Though if it were up to me I'd have done the tests a little bit differently – how about you? Maybe you've got some cars and slopes you could do some tests on?

Oh hang on! Here comes the caretaker on his nightly rounds! I bet he has a play with me and the other cars like he normally does! Byeeeeeeeee!

Name _____

Testing toy cars

Use the table below to record your results for each slope. Measure the distance your car travels from the bottom of each slope and record the distance in cm for each run.

Number of bricks in the slope

	1	2	3	4	5	6
Run 1						
Run 2						
Run 3						

Which slope made your car travel the furthest distance?

_____

Which slope made your car travel fastest?

_____

How do you know that?

_____

_____

_____

_____

Record sheet

Electricity

Science Scheme of Work objectives

Unit 2F: Using electricity

Section 4: Making a circuit

Section 5: Investigating different circuits

Section 6: Making useful circuits

NC: Sc4 1a, 1b, 1c

To learn about simple series circuits involving batteries, wires, bulbs and other components; for example, buzzers and motors. To learn how a switch can be used to break a circuit.

This story is about mice making simple circuits to make their lives more comfortable and safer (from attacks by Tibbles the cat). The children are asked to design, draw and copy diagrams of simple circuits similar to those described in the story.

It is important to let the children know that while **electricity can be dangerous** you are using such small batteries they don't contain enough electrical power to do them any harm. However, playing with larger batteries could give them a powerful painful shock and playing with mains electricity could seriously harm them or even kill them. Explain that electrical devices can become much more dangerous when they are wet. Because of this, even though the small batteries used in the lesson can't do any harm, insist that wherever the children work with their batteries it is completely dry.

You could ask the children why wires are covered in plastic insulating coating and why people working with electricity usually wear rubber boots. When even a small bulb is lit, the filament gets very hot, so you must insist that the children don't touch the bulbs when they are lit as they may burn their skin.

Resources

- Three sequential worksheets (pages 43–45)
- Batteries (WARNING – Do not use rechargeable batteries because these can get very warm if short-circuited)

- Battery cases
- Wires
- Bulbs
- Bulb holders
- Buzzers
- Motors and fans/propellers (Ideal but not essential)

What to do

> What we are learning today is how to light a bulb using a simple circuit.

❑ Tell the children they are going to hear a story about how electricity can be made using a few small items and that it can make a huge difference to the user's life.

❑ Read the story (pages 40–42).

❑ Explain to the children that they are now going to learn how to make simple electrical circuits. Tell them you will be asking them to draw diagrams of the circuits they've made and make some circuits using diagrams they're given as a guide. Let them know that the circuits they will be designing will be similar to the ones that the mice in the story would find useful. (Two circuits and their diagrams of the kinds the children are going to be asked to make are shown on page 46.)

Group work

❑ Ask the children how each of the components used in the story helped make the circuits that the mice used. Show them each of the components as you discuss them. Ask them how they think a switch works (by breaking the circuit) and why a bulb produces light (the thin filament gets so hot it radiates light). Tell them you're going to divide them into groups (the size of the groups will depend on how many components you have). Ask them to build and record some electrical circuits, using the guidelines of the three activity sheets that they have to complete one after the other. (Differentiation in this lesson will be through the outcome of the work they do.) Explain the safety considerations as mentioned in the tinted box, above left.

What I'm looking for is for you to be able to build a simple circuit and draw a simple circuit diagram.

This is because electricity is dangerous and we need to understand how it works.

Extension activity

❑ Ask the children if they can make and then draw (or draw and then make) any other circuits that the mice would have found useful.

❑ Ask them to design a poster promoting safe use of electricity.

❑ The activity sheets should be completed by each group one after the other. Activity sheet 1 requires the children to draw a simple circuit. On Activity sheet 2 children are asked to follow the illustration to help them build a circuit. There is also a table of symbols that might be used in a diagram of a circuit. The children are asked to use the symbols to label the diagram. (These symbols would be useful for the task on the third worksheet.) At this age children don't actually have to know the standard international circuit symbols – these have been included because some children will find them interesting to know. Other children could be encouraged to create their own symbols. What will be most interesting is if any of the children use the symbols given on Activity sheet 2 to complete the circuit diagram they are asked to draw on Activity sheet 3.

Plenary

❑ Look at examples of the circuits the children have made. Ask them why they work. Ask them to remind you why we have to be careful when working with electricity and how we can use electricity safely.

Mouse story

All through the house it was as quiet as
a mouse...

Everything was definitely as quiet as a
mouse in Mr and Mrs Hargreaves' house
because the only thing making a noise
that night **was** a mouse. Sally Mouse
was an unusually clever mouse and a
mouse who was very interested in
science.

Mr and Mrs Hargreaves had a son who
was very very lazy and who never even
bothered to open any of the exciting and
interesting books he got from all his
relatives. So he hadn't noticed how, day by day, Sally had gnawed away a
page of one of his science books and stolen it away into the maze of tunnels
throughout the house where the mice lived.

By reading the pages of Thomas's science book, Sally had learned about all
sorts of interesting things, including electricity. Well, when Thomas received a

home electricity set from one of his uncles,
Sally could hardly contain herself. Thomas
did actually lift the lid off his science set,
grunt at all the tidily arranged contents
and put the lid back on again. It seemed
like far too much work to Thomas to find
out what the bits and pieces inside his kit
actually did. So he wasn't in the least bit
upset by Sally (with the help of a few of
her friends) gnawing her way through the
cardboard lid and gradually removing
wires, batteries, bulbs and other electrical
bits and pieces.

Back inside the mice's tunnels, Sally explained what they'd be able to do with all the equipment they'd run off with.

'These are batteries,' Sally began. 'If we attach wires to them from one end of the battery to the other, electricity will flow out of them.'

The rest of the mice listened politely. So far they didn't understand this thing called electricity that Sally was talking about and anyway it didn't seem to them to matter if it flowed out of a battery or not.

'Then these are the wires,' continued Sally, excitedly. 'They're made from metal because electricity can flow through metal. They're coated in plastic though, so no one gets an electric shock because electricity can't pass through plastic.'

If Sally had looked at the rest of the mice, she would have noticed that the only shocking thing was how little interest they were taking in what she was telling them.

'Now this is a bulb,' said Sally. 'If we connect one of these into a circuit where the electricity from the battery can flow through the wires and the bulb and then back to the battery, it should light up!'

Sally's friends were equally unimpressed… until she connected the bulb and the wires to the battery. When the little bulb suddenly lit up all the mice got very excited! At night time, especially, it got very dark in their tunnels – the mice were always running into each other.

Little bulbs like this would light up the tunnels so everyone could see where they were going!

Then Sally showed them how to connect up a motor in the circuit with a fan attached to it, that helped blow fresh air around the mice's tunnels.

'It's pretty useful, this electricity,' said Roger, one of the other mice. 'Let me see if I can make one of these bulbs light.'

Roger connected a wire to a battery, then a bulb to the wire and then attached another wire to the bulb.

'Hey! Nothing's happening!' said Roger. 'This electricity only works for you!'

'It'll work for you too!' said Sally. 'But the electricity has always got to have a way of getting from one end of the battery to the other! You've got a break in your circuit!' She joined the last wire of Roger's circuit to the back of the battery and, sure enough, the bulb lit up again.

BUZZ!

A little while later, all the tunnels weaving around the house that the mice used had electrical circuits in them. They all had bulbs in them that could be turned on by switches; many of them had motors in them with fans on them to pull in fresh air and one or two of them had a buzzer that could be used as an alarm if Tibbles the cat was on the prowl!

So thanks to Sally's interest in science all the mice lived much more comfortably and safely ever after.

Name _____

Using electricity

Help Roger. Draw a circuit for him that has one bulb in it that would work. You should have practised making one yourself. Make sure he could look at your diagram and be able to copy it.

Name _____

Using electricity

The mice need a circuit that has two bulbs in it and a switch. Can you build it using the drawing below to help you?

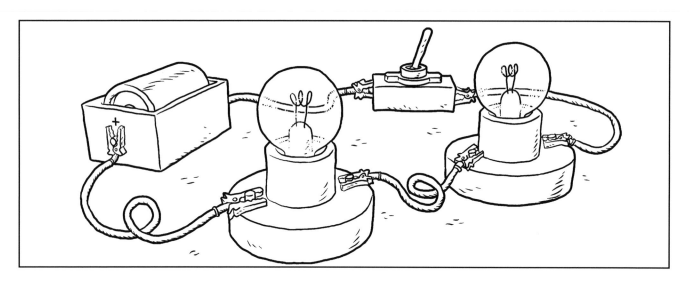

Below is a table of symbols, which are used by scientists to show parts of a circuit on a diagram, and a diagram of the circuit above. Label the diagram. One has been done for you.

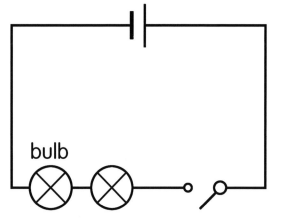

bulb

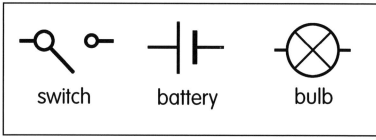

switch   battery   bulb

Table of symbols

Name _____

Using electricity

Set up and draw a circuit that uses a switch and has a buzzer in it that the mice can use when Tibbles is around!

Circuit diagrams

Circuit 1 and its diagram

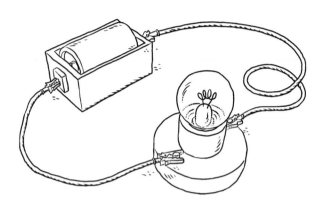
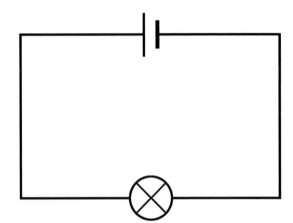

Circuit 2 and its diagram

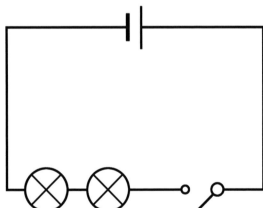

Even fairytale characters need a holiday, especially those who have been around for generations. Usually they got a bit of a rest shortly after Christmas, when Santa Claus could repaint his sleigh and all the pantomime characters could have a rest from shouting, 'Oh no he isn't', 'Oh yes he is' and 'Behind you!'

Finally, though, everyone in Fairyland decided they should build a holiday resort somewhere in Fairyland and have somewhere to go for a proper holiday. So they had a competition to decide where to build it. Lots of the fairy kingdoms entered the competition but in the end only two made it to the final that was to be judged by a special panel of fairytale characters, including Snow White, one of the Three Bears and Captain Hook.

One of the kingdoms was ruled by King Bumble and his daughter Studious. They'd entered the competition because they thought their kingdom, called Expansia, was a perfect site for a holiday resort as it was such a beautiful place and was famous for its joke-telling fish, its beautiful hand-made suitcases and its two main specialities – curry-flavoured ice cream and baked bean-flavoured lemonade.

The other kingdom, called Alkalinia, was ruled by Queen Acidic. If the judges who had voted for her kingdom to get to the final had looked behind the scenes they'd have noticed that her subjects were working like slaves to make everything appear pleasant and beautiful. Like Queen

Acidic herself the beauty of Alkalinia was only skin deep.

As well as making her own kingdom appear far better than it really was, Queen Acidic had used lots of devious tricks to make the other kingdoms and their rulers seem much less well suited to run a holiday resort than her. Queen Acidic was only interested in the money she would make from hundreds of tourists. It wouldn't make things any better for her subjects – maybe even worse – as she already treated them like slaves all the time anyway.

The representatives of each kingdom had to sit in front of the panel of judges and their opponents and explain why they thought their kingdom was most suited to become the Fairyland holiday resort.

Before the final began, Queen Acidic turned up the heating of the room they were going to be in, so by the time everyone was seated it was very very warm.

One of Queen Acidic's favourite tricks was to pretend to be very friendly and to respect her opponents.

'My, isn't it warm in here!' said Queen Acidic, patting her forehead with a handkerchief. 'I think we could all do with some of that excellent and delicious baked bean-flavoured lemonade they make in Expansia. Why, if my kingdom were lucky enough to win, I'd make sure we ordered cases and cases of it for our visitors to enjoy… I've heard it's even more delicious with lots of ice in it. Why don't you put plenty of ice cubes in each glass?'

Well, after having his lemonade so highly complimented by his rival, King Bumble could hardly refuse to give everyone a large glass of baked bean-flavoured lemonade with several ice cubes floating on top. He'd wanted to serve some later on anyway.

His daughter Studious, though, began to get suspicious of Queen Acidic's motives because she knew something about the science of ice cubes and began watching out for tricks. She also put the freezers with their curry-flavoured ice cream in them on their 'Super Freeze' setting.

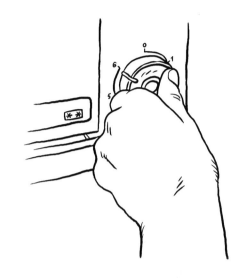

The next trick came straight away. Before anyone had a chance to drink any of the lemonade, Queen Acidic began telling everyone about her seemingly wonderful kingdom. If any of the judges looked like they were lifting their glass to have a drink she would ask them a question so they had to put their drink down and answer it. Everyone apart from Princess Studious was deceived – she'd expected this to happen.

After talking to everyone, or asking questions, in the now very warm room for a while, Queen Acidic suddenly stopped in mid-sentence and looked at her glass of lemonade in horror.

'My goodness!' she declared. 'I don't believe it! I didn't realise that King Bumble had given us such mean portions of lemonade! Look! The lemonade is nowhere near the top of the glass! That must show how mean King Bumble is and how unsuitable he is as a candidate for the manager of a holiday resort!'

Everyone looked at their own glass of lemonade. Even King Bumble couldn't believe it – he was sure he had been careful to give everyone a generous serving to the top of their glass.

'These mean portions must show how mean King Bumble is,' continued Queen Acidic, pressing home her point. 'I think it indicates how unsuitable he would be as the proprietor of a holiday resort because someone running a holiday resort should be naturally generous – not naturally mean like King Bumble seems to be!'

King Bumble almost folded up in his chair because he was so upset and deflated by what had happened. Princess Studious wasn't dispirited though. She bounced out of her chair enthusiastically.

'What's happened to the lemonade doesn't show anything except how generous my father is. Let me just put your lemonade glasses in the freezer while I serve you all a portion of our famous curry-flavoured ice cream!'

Not having had the chance to drink any of the baked bean-flavoured lemonade, the judges were delighted to eat some of the ice-cream, although they still couldn't help thinking that Queen Acidic had been right about the portions of lemonade King Bumble had served them. They were then absolutely astounded when Princess Studious took the glasses out of the freezer and saw that the lemonade, which was now all frozen, was sticking right over the top of the glasses.

'There you are!' declared Princess Studious. 'Now you can really see how generous my father is! He actually served you more than could fit into the glasses but as usual he was too modest to say so!'

Well, after that Queen Acidic didn't have any chance in the competition, however many more tricks she used. It was lucky that Princess Studious knew more about melting and freezing than she did.

So fairytale characters had holidays in Expansia happily ever after.

Holiday resort competition

This was actually the original story the authors produced for the 'Materials' lesson (page 28). However, they realised that for the lesson to work it would be essential for a freezer to be readily available, which isn't the case in all schools.

However, if you do have a freezer you could replicate what happens in the story. A peculiar, though not unique, quality of water is that it expands as it changes its state from a liquid to a solid. (It consequently becomes less dense, which is why ice floats in water.) So you could half fill a glass with water or lemonade and then fill up the glass with ice, host e liquid reaches the top of the glass. Leave the ice to melt – the level of the liquid should drop below the top of the glass. Then put the glass in the freezer. When the liquid has turned to ice, it should have expanded beyond the top of the glass.

(Note: it is best to use a plastic beaker – real glass may shatter with the force of the expanding ice.)